Twenty Most Favourite Songs of Burns

Twenty Most Favourite Songs of Burns

With music, words and notes on
the Lasses to whom they were written

Selected and Presented by
Andrew Winton

Shepheard–Walwyn
London

First published in 1998 by
Shepheard-Walwyn (Publishers) Ltd.
26 Charing Cross Road (Suite 34)
London WC 2H 0DH

ISBN 0 85683 175 1.

Printed in Hong Kong
Through Worldprint

Contents

For Kathleen

"The great misfortune of my life
was never to have an aim."

Foreword

All my life I have looked for things that are bonnie.
Born and brought up in North Lanarkshire, the
moor was my playground for many years.

There, in the long summer days I would disappear
for hours on end ~ time flying by "wi' tentless heed."
There, I explored the long peat hags and shoogie-
bogs, and gathered all kinds of grasses and threshes.
There, I listened to the calls and singing of the
birds, and was able to imitate most of them, ~~~
without understanding.
There, I lay on beds of wild thyme and heathers
beside clear cool burns, and drank the water as it
chuckled over hard white stones ~~~ and ~~~
There, in my Primary School, I was taught to recite
the poems of Robert Burns.

With this background, old Scottish airs came
naturally to me; at a later date, I would play our
simple melodies on my violin (as best I could) and
came to realise how suitable were the words used

by the Bard. I had a great desire to pass on some of the pleasure I got from his songs. To do this I would lay aside the cold hard print of the many books of his works and

I would try to develop a hand of write to suit the subjects.

I would search for the music that is known because he gave us words to sing;

I would endeavour to draw and paint all the flowers and grasses that inspired him when he wandered out to compose; and

I would write a word or two about the lasses to whom the songs were written.

I know that there are many lovers of the works of Burns who know the joy and delight of reading his poetry and singing his songs. To those who do not know ~~~ I would like to think that my efforts might induce them to read and search further. I can assure them that great enjoyments lie ahead; and perhaps, like me, they will wish to pass on the pleasure that comes from words that were written over two hundred years ago.

Introduction

In 1786, Robert Burns was persuaded to go to Edinburgh to seek out a publisher for a second edition of his poems. While there, he met with James Johnson, an engraver and music seller, who had come to the city from the Borders. Johnson had little or no education, but had decided to try to collect the words and music of all existing Scots Songs. When he met Burns, he had published one volume of his Scots Musical Museum. Burns promised to help him and began, with great enthusiasm, to put words to airs and to re-write some of the indelicate rhymes which were being sung at that time.

Three volumes were published before the Bard died, and volume five was at the printer. The sixth ~ and last volume was produced in 1803 ~ seven years later. The Musical Museum is probably the most important collection of Scots songs ever made.

In 1792, Burns met another music enthusiast who was to play a great part in the Bard's decision to compose songs. This was

George Thomson, the son of a Fife school-master. Educated in Dumfermline, he had some legal training and was then recommended for a clerical post with the Board of Trustees for the encouragement of Art and Manufacture in Scotland. He remained with the Board all his life and finished his career as Chief Clerk.

His abiding love in life was music. He played in the orchestra of the St. Cecilia Concerts, and loved to listen to Scots airs sung by continental singers who were visiting Edinburgh at that time. His dream was to publish a book of Select Scottish Airs, and to this end he wrote to Burns explaining his ambitions.

George Thomson to Robert Burns:

Edinburgh, September 1792.

Sir,

For some years past I have, with a friend or two, employed many leisure hours in collating and collecting the most favourite of our national melodies, for publication. We have engaged Pleyel, the most agreeable composer living, to put accompaniments to these and also to compose an instrumental prelude and conclusion to each air, the better to fit them for concerts both public and private. To render this work perfect, we are desirous to have the poetry improved wherever it seems unworthy of the music; and that it is so, in many instances, is allowed by everyone conversant with our musical collections. The editors of these seem in general to have depended on the music proving an excuse for the verses; and hence some charming melodies are united to mere nonsense and doggerel, while others are accommodated with rhymes so loose and indelicate as cannot be sung in decent company. ~~~~~ We shall esteem your poetical assistance a particular favour ~~~~~ Tell me frankly then, whether you will devote your leisure to writing twenty or twenty-five songs, suitable to the particular melodies which I am prepared to send you. A few Songs, exceptionable only in some of their verses, I will likewise submit to your consideration; leaving it to you, either to mend these or make new Songs in their stead. ~~~~

Relying on the letter accompanying this, to be forgiven for the liberty I have taken in in addressing you.

I am, with great esteem,
Sir, your most obedient, humble servant,
G. Thomson.

Burns replied that he would cheerfully do the work so long as he was not to be hurried. By the end of the year he had sent six or seven songs to Thomson. In June, 1793, Thomson produced the first part of his Select Scottish Airs. It contained the first twenty-five songs which Burns had promised. Thomson then decided that he would endeavour to publish every Scottish air worth singing if Burns would continue to write words

Much correspondence followed, but it was not until September '93, when Thomson was harassing the Bard for more songs that Burns responded with a letter describing how he composed his songs ~~ ~~ "until I am compleat master of a tune, in my own singing, (such as it is) I never can compose for it. My way is: I consider the poetic Sentiment correspondent to my idea of the musical expression; then chuse my theme; begin one Stanza; when that is composed, which is generally the most difficult part of the business, I walk out, sit down now and then look out for objects in Nature around me that are in unison or harmony with the cogitations of my fancy and workings of my bosom; humming every now and then the air with the verses I have framed; when I feel my Muse beginning to jade, I retire to the solitary fireside of my study and there commit my effusions to paper; swinging at intervals on the hind legs of my elbow-chair by way of calling forth my own critical strictures as my pen goes"

"Seriously, this at home is almost invariably my way."

"Nae man can tether time or tide"

Ae Fond Kiss
Parting Song to Clarinda

Ae fond kiss and then we sever;
Ae fareweel, and then forever;
Deep in heart-wrung tears I'll pledge thee;
Warring sighs and groans I'll wage thee.
Who shall say that Fortune grieves him?
While the star of hope she leaves him;
Me, nae cheerful twinkle lights me;
Dark despair around benights me.

Burns chose a Gaelic air, Rory Dall's Port for this lyric
Some years later it was discarded for another air
which was favoured for many years. This, in turn,
was changed for another Gaelic air—Hi oro's na horo eile.

Old Highland Melody.

Ae Fond Kiss
Parting Song to Clarinda

I'll ne'er blame my partial fancy,
naething could resist my Nancy:
But to see her was to love her
love but her and love for ever~~
Had we never loved sae kindly,
had we never lov'd sae blindly!
Never met ——or never parted,
we had ne'er been broken-hearted.

Fare-thee weel, thou first and fairest!
fare-thee weel, thou best and dearest!
Thine be ilka joy and treasure,
Peace, Enjoyment, Love and Pleasure!
Ae fond kiss and then we sever;
ae fareweel, alas, for ever!
Deep in heart-wrung tears I'll pledge thee,
warring sighs and groans I'll wage thee.

The words of this song were sent in a letter to
Nancy M'Lehose in 1791, prior to her departure for
the West Indies.

Ae Fond Kiss
Parting Song to Clarinda

In August 1792, it was published in Volume 4 of Johnson's Musical Museum. The air below, blended with, in the words of Sir Walter Scott, "the essence of a thousand love tales" makes it, for me, one of Burns' most exquisite songs.

Ae Fond Kiss
Parting Song to Clarinda

Nancy M'Lehose was born Agnes Craig: her father was a Glasgow surgeon. At the age of seventeen she married James M'Lehose, a young law agent of poor character. After four years she had four children and had left her husband because of his cruelty. When her father died she went to Edinburgh and took up residence in Potter Row. She first met Burns at a tea party in the house of Miss Nimmo, a friend of Margaret Chalmers. There was a mutual attraction and several meetings took place. A correspondence developed between the two and Nancy, in her position as a grass widow, suggested that she should adopt the name of Clarinda and that Robert should therefore be Sylvander. "Ae fond Kiss" was written for Nancy when she decided to go to Jamaica in an attempt at a reconciliation with her husband. She found, however, that he had a mistress there, and returned to Scotland where she died in 1844 in her eighty third year.

Had we never loved sae kindly,
had we never loved sae blindly;
never met or never pairted
we had ne'er been broken-hearted.

Thine be ilka joy and treasure
Peace, Enjoyment, Love and Pleasure.

Afton Water

Flow gently, sweet Afton, amang thy green braes,
flow gently, I'll sing thee a song in thy praise:
My Mary's asleep by thy murmuring stream,
flow gently, sweet Afton, disturb not her dream.

Thou stock dove whose echo resounds thro' the glen,
ye wild whistling blackbirds, in yon thorny den,
Thou green crested lapwing thy screaming forbear,
I charge you, disturb not my slumbering Fair.

How lofty, sweet Afton, thy neighbouring hills,
far marked with the courses of clear winding rills;
There daily I wander as noon rises high,
my flocks and my Mary's sweet cot in my eye.

How pleasant thy banks and green valleys below,
where wild in the woodlands the primroses grow,
There oft, as mild ev'ning weeps over the lea,
the sweet-scented birk shades my Mary and me.

Afton Water

Thy crystal stream, Afton, how lovely it glides,
and winds by the cot where my Mary resides;
How wanton thy waters her snowy feet lave,
as gath'ring sweet flowerets, she stems thy clear wave.

Flow gently, sweet Afton, amang thy green braes,
flow gently, sweet river, the theme of my lays;
My Mary's asleep by thy murmuring stream,
flow gently, sweet Afton, disturb not her dream.

Afton Water

Afton Water is a small burn that flows into the Nith River near New Cumnock. It forms a lovely valley, and is over looked by richly sylvan banks.

Melody composed by A. Hume.

Slow and tenderly.

Afton Water

This song appears in Vol. IV of the Musical Museum. There is some dubiety as to whom it was written, but Gilbert Burns had no doubt it was for Highland Mary. Burns probably met Mary Campbell when she was a nursemaid in the home of his friend Gavin Hamilton in Mauchline. Early 1786 was a very unsettled period of his life, and so he made tentative arrangements to emigrate to the West Indies. When Jean Armour was sent away by her parents to Paisley, Burns turned seriously to Mary.

On a Sunday in May of that year, they met on the Banks of Ayr, exchanged Bibles, and solemnly made marriage vows. Mary then went off to the West Highlands to return later to Greenock. Within days of returning, however, she contracted a malignant fever, and died. This beautiful lyric is one of four that Burns wrote for Highland Mary.

"Flow gently, sweet river,
Disturb not her dream."

"I have...... employed many leisure hours
in collating and collecting the most
favourite of our national melodies."
Thomson to Burns.

"— — — devote your leisure hours to writing twenty or twenty-five songs."

A Health to Ane I Lo'e Dear

The last six months of the Bard's life
were distressful. In a letter to Thomson in early July,
he wrote ~~~~ "besides my inveterate rheumatism, my
appetite is quite gone: and I am so emaciated as to be
scarce able to support myself on my own legs."
Mrs. Walter Riddell invited him to dinner and sent her
carriage for him as he was unable to walk. Writing to
a friend she states, "The stamp of death was imprinted
on his features ~~~~ his first salutation was, "Well
Madam, have you any commands for the other world?"
All this time he was being cared for by
Jessy Lewars, a lass of eighteen years, a sister of a
brother Exciseman who lived in a house across the
street in Dumfries. There is no doubt that 'A health
to ane I lo'e dear' was written especially for her. In
brighter moments in gloomy days, the Bard would
scribble complimentary verses to Jessy. Written in
May, 1796, this song was amongst the last sent
to Thomson before his death in July ~~~ a last
expression of gratitude to someone he admired
and loved dearly.

A Health to Ane I Lo'e Dear

Here's a health to ane I lo'e dear,
here's a health to ane I lo'e dear,
Thou art sweet as the smile when
                fond lovers meet,
and saft as their parting tear—Jessy.
Altho' thou maun never be mine
    altho' even hope is denied;
'Tis sweeter for thee despairing,
than aught in the world beside—Jessy.

I mourn thro' the gay, gaudy day,
as hopeless I muse on thy charms;
But welcome the dream o' sweet slumber,
for then I am lockt in thine arms—Jessy.

I guess by the dear angel smile,
    I guess by the love-rolling e'e;
But why urge the tender confession,
'gainst Fortune's fell cruel decree—Jessy.

A Health to Ane I Lo'e Dear

In May 1796, Burns wrote to Thomson, "I once mentioned to you an air which I have long admired, "Here's a health to them that's awa' hiney" but I forget if you took any notice of it. I have just been trying to suit it with verses; I beg leave to recommend the air to your attention once more."

Andantino   Tune: Here's a health to ane that's awa

A Health to Ane I Lo'e Dear

After the death of the Bard, Jessy Lewars looked after the Burns family for some time, helping Jean with her four children through the hard times. She took Robert, the eldest boy, into her own home for a year. In 1799 she married James Thomson, a writer in Dumfries, and had two daughters and five sons. On the death of her husband in 1849, Jessy moved to the village of Maxwelltown, where she died in 1855 in her seventy-eighth year. She is buried close to the Burns Mausoleum — the tombstone of the Thomsons being fixed in the south side of it.

On June 16th, James Johnson received a letter from Burns ~~~ 'my wife has a very particular friend of hers, a young lady who sings well to whom she wishes to present the Scots Musical Museum. If you have a spare copy, will you be so obliging as to send it by the very first Fly, as I am anxious to have it soon.'

In answer to his request, Johnson sent three copies of the Museum, one of which the Poet presented to Jessy. In this way did Robert Burns show his gratitude to a warm caring Jessy Lewars.

I have some favourite flowers in Spring,
among which are the mountain daisy, the
harebell, the foxglove, the wild brier rose,
the budding birch and the hoary
hawthorn that I view and hang over with
particular delight.

I never hear the loud solitary whistle of the
curlew in a Summer noon, or the mixing
cadence of a troup of gray plovers in an
Autumn morning without feeling an
elevation of soul like the enthusiasm of
devotion or poetry.

A Rosebud by my Early Walk

A rose bud by my early walk,
Adoon a corn-inclosèd bawk,
Sae gently bent its thorny stalk,
    All on a dewy morning.
Ere twice the shades o' dawn are fled,
In a' its crimson glory spread,
And drooping rich the dewy head,
    It scents the early morning.

Within the bush her cover'd nest,
A little linnet fondly prest;
The dew sat chilly on her breast
    Sae early in the morning.
She soon shall see her tender brood,
The pride, the pleasure o' the wood,
Amang the fresh green leaves bedew'd
    Awake the early morning.

So thou, dear bird, young Jenny fair,
On trembling string or vocal air
Shall sweetly pay the tender care,
    That tents thy early morning.

A Rosebud by my Early Walk

In the autumn of the year 1787,
Burns went on tour to the North of
Scotland with William Nicol, the
classics master of the High School, Edinburgh. Returning to the Capital, Nicol
introduced the Bard to a colleague,
William Cruikshank, who lived at No 2
St. James Square; Burns took up lodgings
there. Cruikshank had an only daughter
Jenny, who, at the age of twelve, was a
very promising pianist.

Burns spent many happy hours
listening to Jenny playing and singing
his favourite airs, and it was here that he
adapted many of his new verses to old airs
for the Scots Musical Museum.

The 'Rosebud' was created as
a compliment to Jenny. The air was composed
by David Sillar, "a brither poet" who at that
time, was a schoolmaster in Irvine. To Jenny,
Burns also wrote "Beauteous rosebud young and
gay." She became Mrs Henderson and lived in Jedburgh.

A Rosebud by my Early Walk

So thou sweet Rosebud, young and gay,
Shall beauteous blaze upon the day,
And bless the parents' evening ray
That watched thy early morning.

Tune:- The Shepherd's wife.

A Rosebud by my Early Walk

It was when living at 2. St. James Square that a Josiah Walker visited the Bard. Many years later, Walker was to write, "About the end of October, I called for him at the house of a friend whose daughter, though not more than twelve, was a considerable proficient in music. I found him seated by the harpsichord of this young lady, listening with the keenest interest to his own verses, which she sung with accomplishment and adjusting them to the music by repeated trials of the effect. In this occupation he was so totally absorbed that it was difficult to draw his attention from it for a moment."

This gives us some idea of the care and study bestowed by Burns upon his songs which resulted in their almost perfect adaption to their respective airs.

"The warmest, richest, most tender
and most sensuous love songs that
any poet has given to the world."

"This delicious passion I hold to be
our dearest pleasure here below."

Ay Waukin O

This is a very old song. David Herd has a fragment
in his Ancient and Modern Scottish Songs which
is probably part of the original:

O wat· wat~~~~ O wat and weary·
Sleep I can get nane·
For thinking on my deary·
A' the night I wake~~A' the day I weary
Sleep I can get nane
For thinking on my deary·

In Robert Chambers 'Songs of Scotland,' there is a
modern version (1829) of the song which ends with
these lines:

O for Friday nicht·
Friday in the gloamin',
O for Friday nicht·
Friday's lang in comin'·

Ay Waukin O

Slow, with much expression

Ay Waukin O

Ay waukin O
Waukin still and weary
Sleep I can get nane
For thinking on my dearie.

Simmer's a pleasant time
flowers o' every colour;
The water rins in the heugh,
and I long for my true lover.

When I sleep I dream,
when I wauk I'm eerie,
Sleep I can get nane
For thinking on my dearie.

Lanely nicht comes on,
a' the lave are sleepin';
I think on my dear lad
and bleer my een wi' greetin'.

Ay Waukin O

Burns made only a few alterations to this old song. The words of the first and last verses are definitely his. Two versions, no. 213, and no 382 were sent to Johnson for his Museum with the air in triple time. In his Select Scottish Airs Thomson set the melody in common time, the form adopted now.

This little song contains, for me, all the truth of feeling, simplicity and grace of expression and passionate tenderness, to be found in many of our very old songs.
Usually sung by a lady, I recall one Burns evening in Liberton Hospital, that when Gwen sang the last line ---"and I bleer my een wi' greetin'" there was scarcely a dry eye in the hall.

"She bade me sing the loves, the joys, the rural scenes and rural pleasures of my native soil ~~~~in my native tongue."

"Whatever may be my failings, for failings are a part of human nature, may they ever be those of a generous heart and an independent mind."

Bonnie Wee Thing

Deborah Davies, the daughter of Dr Daniel Davies of Tenby in Pembrokeshire, was distantly related to the Riddles of Glen Carse, a neighbouring farm to Ellisland. Burns met her there and was greatly attracted. In a letter to Mrs Dunlop he writes of her as "positively the least creature ever I saw to be at the same time unexceptionably, and indeed uncommonly, handsome and beautiful."

The story is told that one day when Burns was in Moffat, Deborah rode past, accompanied by a tall lady; on a friend asking the Bard why God made one lady so large and the other so little, he replied with an epigram:

"Ask why God made the gem so small,
And why so huge the granite?
Because God meant mankind should set
That higher value on it."

Bonnie Wee Thing

Bonnie wee thing, cannie wee thing,
Lovely wee thing, wert thou mine,
I wad wear thee in my bosom,
Lest my jewel it should tine.

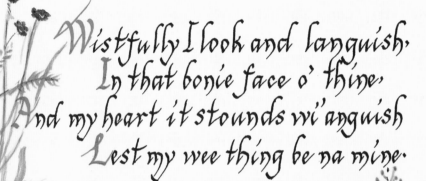

Wistfully I look and languish,
In that bonie face o' thine,
And my heart it stounds wi' anguish
Lest my wee thing be na mine.

Wit and Grace, and Love and Beauty,
In ae constellation shine;
To adore thee is my duty
Goddess o' this soul o' mine!

Bonnie wee thing, cannie wee thing
Lovely wee thing, wert thou mine;
I wad wear thee in my bosom,
Lest my jewel it should tine.

Bonnie Wee Thing

Andante   Tune:- The bonnie wee thing.

This song "was composed on my
little idol, the charming lovely Davies,"
probably about 1790. The air is very old,
and goes back to an original, with the
same name, in a Manuscript dated 1627.
It first appeared in the Museum in 1792.

Bonnie Wee Thing

Deborah was courted by a Captain Delany. According to Cunningham, "he made himself acceptable to her by sympathising in her pursuits, and writing verses on her ~~~~~ An offer of marriage was made and accepted ~~~~but Delany's circumstances were urged as an obstacle: delays ensued, a coldness on the lover's part followed; his regiment was called abroad, and he went with it; she heard from him once, and no more: and was left to mourn the change of affection~~~ to droop and die."

Delaney perished in battle soon after the death of the young lady, of whose love he was so unworthy.

"To spare thee noo is past my pow'r
Thou bonnie gem!"

"I never had the least thought or inclination
of turning Poet till I got once heartily
in Love."

44

"and then rhyme and song were,
in a manner, the spontaneous
language of my heart."

Ca' the Yowes to the Knowes

Ca' the yowes tae the knowes,
Ca' them whare the heather growes,
Ca' them whare the burnie rowes,
My bonnie dearie.

Hark the mavis' e'ening sang,
Sounding Cludin's woods amang;
Then a-faulding let us gang,
My bonnie dearie.

We'll gae doon by Cludin side
Thro' the hazels spreading wide,
O'er the waves that sweetly glide,
To the moon sae clearly.

Yonder Cluden's silent towers,
Whare at moonshines midnight hours
O'er the dewy bending flowers,
Fairies dance sae cheerie.

Ca' the Yowes to the Knowes

Ghaist nor bogle shalt thou fear,
Thou'rt to Love and Heav'n sae dear,
Nocht of ill may come thee near,
My bonnie Dearie.

Fair and lovely as thou art,
Thou hast stown my very heart;
I can die --- but canna part,
My bonnie Dearie.

Ca'the Yowes to the Knowes

"In a solitary stroll which I took to-day, I tried my hand on a few pastoral lines, following up the idea of the chorus which I would preserve. Here it is with all its crudities and imperfections on its head." Quoted from his letter to Johnston in 1794.

Ca'the Yowes to the Knowes

The original song of Ca' the Yowes is attributed to Tibbie Pagan who lived in the Muirkirk area, and died in 1821 aged eighty. Her version of the song had several verses which had never appeared in print until Burns sent it to Johnson for the Musical Museum. One of Jean's favourite songs, Burns reset it with verses of his own before sending it to Thomson in 1794 with explanitory notes.

In a countryside well known for prize tups, it is not surprising that this was a favourite bothy song.

I well remember one evening, Davie, the herd was at the open door when Jenny, the new maid, was passing. She stopped to listen -- In a clear tenor voice, Davie sang the chorus, looking straight into Jenny's eyes. When he finished, there was a pause, then Jenny blushed gently and nodded. In the gloaming Davie and Jenny strolled down the burnside hand in hand.

"Whatever mitigates the woes or increases the happiness of others, this is my criterion of goodness"

"And whatever injures society at large,
or any individual in it,
this is my measure of iniquity."

Green Grow the Rashes, O

"Green grow the rashes" comes from a very old fragment, which is, however, so indelicate that it is not desirable to quote even one of its three verses. Burns mentions it in his first Commonplace Book in August 1784.

The song is an improvement on an old ditty that was sung to the same air. The last verse was added at a later date, probably when he was at Ellisland, and relates to an old comedy entitled Cupid's Whirligig, which was published in 1607. The passage is as follows:—

"Oh woman ———————————— since we were made before ye, should we not love and Admire ye as the last, and therefore perfect'st work of Nature? Man was made when Nature was But an apprentice, but woman, when she Was a skilful mistress of her Art."

52

Green Grow the Rashes. O.

Green grow the rashes, O!
Green grow the rashes, O!
The sweetest hours that e'er I spend,
Are spent amang the lasses, O!

There's nocht but care on every han',
on every hour that passes O;
What signifies the life o' man,
an' 'twer' na' for the lasses, O?

The warly race may riches chase,
an' riches still may fly them O;
And tho' at last they catch them fast,
their hearts can ne'er enjoy them O.

Gi'e me a cannie hour at e'en,
my arms aboot my dearie, O;
An' warly cares, an' warly men,
may a' gae tapsal teerie, O.

Green Grow the Rashes O.

Cheerily   We're a dry wi' drinkin o't.

For you sae douce, ye sneer at this;
Ye're nocht but senseless asses, O.
The wisest man the warl e'er saw,
he dearly lo'ed the lasses, O.

Auld Nature swears, the lovely dears
her noblest work she classes, O:
Her 'prentice han' she try'd on man,—
an' then she made the lasses, O.

Green Grow the Rashes O.

Words from the song are quoted at almost every Burns supper. The lass who replies to the toast to the lassies, invariably recites the last verse (amid loud cheers) to show the superiority of lasses to laddies!

The air in three-four time, makes a popular waltz. I remember once, in a P.O.W. camp concert during the last war that I sang this song before an audience of men who had not had contact with lassies for some three four or five years. There was evidence of sentiment and emotion, and when I asked them to join in the chorus, they did so with heartfelt fervour: so we sang it twice!

On morning parade, it was announced that the commandant had enjoyed the concert but the song with the chorus was banned from all future shows. "It was disturbing the prisoners too much." Needless to say, it was sung with great verve and joy the following evening. The result was ten days solitary on bread and water in the cooler, and I was permitted to sing "Green Grow the Rashes O." as much as I wished — all to myself.

I can affirm, both from bachelor and wedlock experience that Love is the Alpha and Omega of human enjoyment.

Love, thou hast pleasures, and deep
                                    ha'e I luv'd;
Love, thou hast sorrows, and sair
                                    ha'e I pruv'd.

John Anderson My Jo.

Set to a very old tune called "John Anderson, My Jo," this song was one of the first Burns sent to Johnson for Vol. 2 of his Musical Museum. According to tradition, the original John Anderson is said to have been the town piper of Kelso. Be that as it may, in Bishop Percy's manuscript book of ballads, produced in the middle of the 16th century, these verses are to be found: ~~~

John Anderson my jo, cum in as ze gae by,
and zee sall get a sheep's heid weel baken in a pye.
Weel baken in a pye, and a haggis in a pat,
John Anderson my jo, cum in and zes get that.

And how doe ye, cummer? and how doe ye thrive?
and how many bairns hae ye? cummer I hae five.
Are they to your awin gudeman? Na cummer na~
for three o' them were gotten quhan Wullie was awa.

From 1795 until 1798, a collection of selected poetry was published by a respectable publishing firm in Glasgow. William Reid, one of the partners, attempted several additional stanzas to the original John Anderson, but these were inferior to the words of Burns.

58

John Anderson My Jo.

John Anderson, my jo, John
When we were first acquent;
Your locks were like the raven,
Your bonie brow was brent;
But now your brow is beld, John,
Your locks are like the snaw;
But blessings on your frosty pow
John Anderson, my jo.

John Anderson, my jo, John,
We clamb the hill thegither;
And mony a cantie day John,
We've had wi' ane anither:
Noo we maun totter doon, John,
But hand in hand we'll go,
And sleep thegither at the fit
John Anderson, my jo.

In two stanzas, Burns created what has been
described as "the most beautiful idyll of happy
married life that ever was written".

John Anderson My Jo.

John Anderson My Jo.

There are some who would say that Burns was thinking of his own father and mother when he was writing this song.

The theme, however, is old, and I would like to think that in paying this tribute, he had many elderly folks in mind. Every village had its own favourite walk and elderly lovers would stroll out in the gloaming to savour the peace and tranquility of the evening when the day's darg was done ~~~~
~~~"and we'll sleep thegether at the foot
John Anderson, my jo."

But a' the pleasures e'er I saw,
Though three times doubled fairly;
That happy nicht was worth them a'
        amang the rigs o' barley.

Though losses and crosses,
Be lessons right severe;
There's wit there ye'll get there,
Ye'll find nae ither where.

Mary Morison

O Mary at thy window be,
It is the wished, the trysted hour!
Those smiles and glances let me see
That make the miser's treasure poor;
How blythely wad I bide the stoure,
A weary slave frae sun to sun,
Could I the rich reward secure,
The lovely Mary Morison.

There is some doubt as to whom this song
was written. Burns states that "it was one of my
juvenile works," and was probably composed around
1784, when he would be twenty-five. In Mauchline
there was a lass named Mary Morison of some
thirteen or fourteen years. It seems unlikely that
Burns would be writing such a song for her. According
to Mrs Begg, his youngest sister, he was courting
Alison or Ellison Begbie, the daughter of a farmer,
who worked as a servant in a house near the Cessnock
River. The view of many of Burns' biographers is
that the words Mary Morison are a euphonious
rendering of Alison Begbie.

Mary Morison

Yestreen, when to the trembling string
The dance gaed through the lighted ha',
To thee my fancy took its wing,
I sat but neither heard nor saw:
Tho' this was fair and that was braw
And yon the toast of a' the town,
I sighed, and said amang them a',
"Ye are na Mary Morison."

"Of all the productions of Burns, the pathetic and serious love songs which he has left behind him in the manner of old ballads are perhaps those which take the deepest and most lasting hold of the mind. Such are the lines to Mary Morison."
Quoted from Hazlitt.

Oh, Mary, canst thou wreck his peace,
Wha for thy sake wad gladly die?
Or canst thou break that heart of his
Whase only faut is loving thee?
If love for love thou wilt na gie,
At least be pity to me shown;
A thought ungentle canna be
The thought o' Mary Morison.

Mary Morison

When Burns sent this song to Thomson in 1793, he put it to the tune 'Duncan Davidson'. Thomson, however, published it to the tune 'Bide ye yet'. At a later date it was changed again, but it is now sung to ~~~ 'The Miller'.

Asked by Thomson who Mary Morison was, Gilbert Burns replied that she was the lass in 'I'll kiss thee yet, yet'. As this is the chorus to the song 'Bonnie Peggie Alison', it would appear that Mary Morison, Peggy Alison, and Alison Begbie were all three, one and the same.

Mary Morison

Ellison Begbie refused Burns' offer of marriage: she married another and moved to Glasgow. It is interesting to note that Cromek, in his Reliques of Burns which was published in 1808, states that he heard the song On Cessnock Banks "from the oral communication of a lady residing in Glasgow, whom the bard in early life affectionately admired." This could only have been Ellison. Who else would be singing this song?

In Mauchline kirkyaird there is a tombstone with the inscription: "In memory of Adj. John Morrison of the 104th Regiment, who died at Mauchline, 16th April 1804, in the 80th year of his age.

'also his daughter Mary
the poet's bonie Mary Morrison —
who died 29th June 1791
aged 20.

A sister of Mary, who lived to be a grandmother, often spoke of this long-lost Mary, who died in early youth, from the amputation of a foot, accidentally injured, as
"one of the fairest creatures
the sun ever shone upon."

I sighed and said amang them a',
"Ye are na Mary Morison."

Her face is fair, her heart is true;
As spotless as she's bonnie, O.
The op'ning gowan wat wi' dew,
Nae purer is than Nannie, O.

My Nannie's Awa'

In the autumn of 1791, Nancy M'Lehose decided that she would go to Jamaica to see if she could be persuaded to stay with her husband. Before she left on the 6th of December, she, as Clarinda, wrote to her Sylvander, asking him "to let the scenes of nature remind him of Clarinda." Burns replied, "There is one passage in your charming letter — 'tis where you bid the scenes of nature remind me of Clarinda. I shall certainly steal it, and set it in some future poetic production, and get immortal fame by it."

The result was "My Nannie's Awa'" which makes me inclined to believe that it was composed in the summer of 1792, but not sent to Thomson until '94.

When the 'Roselle' docked in Jamaica there was no-one to meet Nancy: her husband had a negro mistress who had borne him a daughter. Complaining of the excessive heat, and the great annoyance of mosquitoes, Nancy returned to Scotland on the same ship on its return journey some three months later.

My Nannie's Awa'

Now in her green mantle blythe Nature arrays,
And listens the lambkins that bleat o'er the braes,
While birds warble welcome in ilka green shaw,
But to me it's delightless — my Nannie's awa'.
But to me it's delightless — my Nannie's awa'.

The snawdrap and primrose our woodlands adorn,
And violets bathe in the weet o' the morn;
They pain my sad bosom, sae sweetly they blaw,
They mind me o' Nannie — and Nannie's awa'.
They mind me o' Nannie — and Nannie's awa'.

Thou lav'rock that springs frae the dews of the lawn,
The shepherd to warn o' the grey-breaking dawn,
And thou mellow mavis that hails the night-fa'
Give over for pity — my Nannie's awa'.
Give over for pity — my Nannie's awa'.

Come Autumn, sae pensive, in yellow and grey,
And soothe me wi' tidings o' Nature's decay;
The dark, dreary Winter, and wild-driving snaw
Alane can delight me — now Nannie's awa'.
Alane can delight me — now Nannie's awa'.

My Nannie's Awa'

This very popular song was undoubtedly composed for Nancy M'Lehose. The melody to which it is sung was composed by Alexander Hume, who also created the equally beautiful air of Afton Water. The song was sent to Thomson in December 1794.

Plaintively   Music by A. Hume.

My Nannie's Awa'

It is easy to imagine the Bard in walks around Ellisland, composing this very popular song: wild flowers grow everywhere; the air is filled with the song of birds ~~~ bringing to mind his word to Thomson "I walk out ~ look out for objects in Nature around me that are in unison or harmony with ---- the workings of my bosom."

And the haunting air to which it is sung ~~ "There'll never be peace till Jamie comes hame" turns the hearts of Burns lovers all over the world.

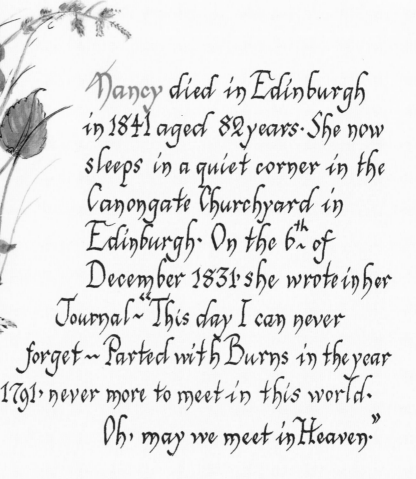

Nancy died in Edinburgh in 1841 aged 82 years. She now sleeps in a quiet corner in the Canongate Churchyard in Edinburgh. On the 6th of December 1831 she wrote in her Journal ~ "This day I can never forget ~ Parted with Burns in the year 1791, never more to meet in this world. Oh, may we meet in Heaven."

Thou art sweet as the smile when
                    fond lovers meet,
And saft as their parting tear--Jessie.

"and I would pour delight on the heart
that could kindly forgive
and generously love."

I Love My Jean
Of a' the Airts the Wind can Blaw

In June 1788, Burns leased the farm of Ellisland in Dumfrieshire. As the steading had to be re-built, it was arranged that Jean would stay at Mauchline and he would work on the site. He lived in an old hovel on the outskirts of the farm, and every day he worked the land and helped in the building. Back in his smoke-filled hut in the evening, he wrote letters or "brushed up some old songs for Johnson's Musical Museum." In Volume three there appears Of a' the Airts, which was composed at this time. A note with it states, "This song I composed out of compliment to Mrs. Burns; it was" he archly added, "during the honey-moon."

There are only two verses in the original version, but two additional stanzas were produced some years later by John Hamilton, a music seller in Edinburgh. They are generally sung to lengthen the song, but are considered to be inferior to the original verses of Burns.

I Love My Jean
Of a' the Airts the Wind can Blaw

Of a' the airts the wind can blaw
I dearly like the west;
For there the bonie Lassie lives
The lassie I lo'e best.
There's wild-woods grow and rivers row
And mony a hill between;
But day and night my fancy's flight,
Is ever wi' my Jean.

I see her in the dewy flowers,
I see her sweet and fair;
I hear her in the tunefu' birds,
I hear her charm the air.
There's not a bonie flower that springs
By fountain, shaw or green;
There's not a bonie bird that sings
But minds me o' my Jean.

I Love My Jean

Tune: Miss Admiral Gordon's Strathspey
Air: Air by William Marshall who
was butler to the Duke of Gordon.

I Love My Jean
Of a' the Airts the Wind can Blaw

Blaw, blaw ye wastlin' winds, blaw saft,
Amang the leafy trees
Wi' gentle gale, frae muir and dale,
Bring hame the laden bees;
And bring the lassie back to me
That's aye sae neat and clean,
Ae smile o' her wad banish care
Sae charming is my Jean.

What sighs and vows amang the knowes,
Hae passed atween us twa!
How fond to meet, how fain to part
That day she gaed awa,
The Powers abune can only ken
To whom this heart is seen,
That nane can be sae dear tae me,
As my sweet lovely Jean.

Regarding these two verses, Dr Chalmers
states ~~ "their inferiority to Burns's lines
is painfully obvious"~~ but I like them!

Nae treasures nor pleasures
could mak' us happy lang;
The heart aye's the part aye,
that makes us richt or wrang.

O gear will buy me rigs o' land,
and gear will buy me sheep and kye;
But the tender heart o' leesom love,
the gowd and siller canna buy.

O Wert Thou in the Cauld Blast

In November 1791, Burns left the farm at Ellisland and took up house in Mill Vennel in Dumfries. Across the street lived John Lewars, a brother Excise Officer and his sister Jessy. A strong family friendship developed and during his last illness, Jessy helped to nurse the poet, and gave Jean, who was expecting another wee one, a helping hand with her four children.

Visiting his friends one day, Burns listened to Jessy singing. "Play it again Jessy," he said, "and I'll see if I can give you some new words." Jessy played an old air until he had absorbed the music completely. Some time later, he handed her the words ~ ~ "O wert thou in the cauld blast."

Some thirty years later, when Jessy was a widow, the verses were shown to Felix Mendelssohn who was visiting Scotland at this time. Recognising the depth of emotion in the words, he set them to the exquisite air which is usually sung to-day. Jessy died in 1855 aged seventy-seven. She married, lived in Dumfries and had seven of a family.

O Wert Thou in the Cauld Blast

O wert thou in the cauld blast
    on yonder lea, on yonder lea,
My plaidie to the angry airt
    I'd shelter thee, I'd shelter thee.
Or did Misfortune's bitter storms,
    aroond thee blaw, aroond thee blaw,
Thy bield should be my bosom
    to share it a', to share it a'.

Or were I in the wildest waste,
    sae bleak and bare, sae bleak and bare;
The desert were a Paradise,
    if thou wert there, if thou wert there.
Or were I Monarch of the globe
    wi' thee to reign, wi' thee to reign,
The brightest jewel in my crown,
    wad be my Queen, wad be my Queen.

In the Book of Scottish Song by Alex Whitelaw, this
sweet little song, headed "Address to a Lady" is set
to the tune of "The Lass o Livingston." It does not
compare to the lovely air by Mendelssohn.

O Wert Thou in the Cauld Blast

Air by

Mendelssohn

Andante.

O Wert Thou in the Cauld Blast

'The Wren's Nest', the song that was sung
to Burns, is number 406 in the Scots Musical
Museum.   This is the song that Jessy sang:

The Robin to the Wren's nest
Cam keekin' in, cam keekin';
O weel's me on your auld pow,
Wad ye be in? wad ye be in?
Ye'se ne'er get leave to lie withoot
And I within, and I within,
Sae langs I hae an auld cloot
To rowe ye in, to rowe ye in.

"The wan moon is setting
behind the white wave,
and time is setting with me, O."

The silly tenderness ~~~ the frustrated passion of the blood ~~ the hopelessness ~~ the dizziness of being in Love.

The Lass o' Ballochmyle

'Twas even~ the dewy fields were green,
on every blade the pearls hang;
The zephyr wantoned round the bean
and bore its fragrant sweets alang:
In every glen the mavis sang,
all nature listening seemed the while,
Except where greenwood echoes rang
amang the braes o' Ballochmyle.

Ballochmyle is an estate on the banks of the river Ayr near
Mauchline. In a letter, Burns says, "I had roved out as
chance directed, on the favorite haunts of my Muse, the
banks of Ayr, to view nature in all the gaiety of the
vernal year."

With careless step I onward strayed,
my heart rejoiced in nature's joy;
When musing in a lonely glade
a maiden fair I chanced to spy:
Her look was like the morning's eye,
her air like nature's vernal smile,
Perfection whispered, passing by,
"Behold the lass o' Ballochmyle."

The Lass o' Ballochmyle

This song was set by Burns to the air
Ettrick Banks, but is now generally
sung to a melody by William Jackson.

Verses three and four are sung more often than the
others ~~ everybody sings "the bonnie lass, the bonnie
bonnie lass ~~ the bonnie lass of Ballochmyle.

The Lass o' Ballochmyle

Fair is the morn in flowery May
and sweet is night in Autumn mild,
When roving thro' the garden gay
or wandering in the lonely wild:
But woman, nature's darling child
there all her charms she does compile:
Ev'n there her other works are foil'd
by the bonny lass o' Ballochmyle.

"The evening sun was flaming o'er the distant western
hills; not a breath stirred the crimson opening blossom,
or the verdant spreading leaf. 'Twas a golden moment
for a poetic heart. I listened to the feathered warblers
pouring their harmony on every hand."

O had she been a country maid,
and I the happy country swain;
Tho' sheltered in the lowest shed,
that ever rose on Scotland's plain!
Thro' weary winter's wind and rain,
with joy, with rapture, I would toil;
And nightly to my bosom strain: and nightly to my bosom strain
the bonny lass o' Ballochmyle. the bonny lass o' Ballochmyle.

The Lass o' Ballochmyle

Then pride might climb the slippry steep;
where fame and honours lofty shine;
And thirst of gold might tempt the deep,
or downward seek the Indian mine;
Give me the cot below the pine,
to tend the flocks or till the soil
And every day have joys divine
with the bonny lass o' Ballochmyle.

The lass was Wilhelmina Alexander, sister of the
Laird. One evening, while taking a walk after her dinner
she came upon a stranger who was leaning in deep
meditation against a tree. A little startled, she
recovered, and passed on. The stranger, of course, was
Burns, who, on his homeward stroll, composed a song
which he sent to the lady with a letter of explanation.
At the time, no notice was taken, but in later years,
Wilhelmina set a high value on the compliment and
showed both the letter and song with great pride on
many occasions. She never married and died in 1843,
fifty seven years after meeting the Poet.
Her descendants erected a rustic bower
where the meeting took place.

The best-laid schemes o' mice an' men
                        Gang aft agley,
An' lea'e us nocht but grief an' pain
                        For promis'd joy!

But och! I backword cast my e'e
On prospects drear!
And forward; tho' I canna see~~
I guess and fear!

My Ain Kind Dearie
The Lea Rig

This is one of the first songs sent by Burns to George Thomson for his Select Scottish Airs. Only one verse of the original manuscript remains. Robert Ferguson, whose poems had a great influence on the work of Burns, had a version founded on this ditty ~~~

I'll rowe thee o'er the lea-rig,
My ain kind dearie O,
I'll rowe thee o'er the lea-rig,
My ain kind dearie O;
Altho' the nicht were ne'er sae wet,
And I were ne'er sae wearie O,
I'll rowe thee o'er the lea-rig,
My ain kind dearie O.

Thomson was well pleased with "My Ain Kind Dearie"; he only found fault with it for being too short ~ a defect Burns remedied by adding another verse to his original thoughts.

My Ain Kind Dearie
The Lea Rig

When o'er the hill the e'ening star
Tells bughtin time is near, my jo,
And owsen frae the furrow'd field
Return sae dowf and wearie O;
    Doun by the burn where scented birks
    Wi' dew are hanging clear my jo,
      I'll meet thee on the lea rig,
        My ain kind dearie, O.

In mirkest glen, at midnicht hour
I'd rove, and ne'er be eerie, O,
If thro' the glen I gaed to thee,
My ain kind dearie, O;
    Altho' the nicht were ne'er sae wild,
    And I were ne'er sae wearie O,
      I'll meet thee on the lea-rig
        My ain kind dearie, O.

My Ain Kind Dearie
The Lea Rig

The hunter lo'es the morning sun,
To rouse the mountain deer my jo,
At noon the fisher seeks the glen,
Adoun the burn to steer, my jo.
Gi'e me the hour o' gloamin' gray,
It mak's my heart sae cheerie·O
To meet thee on the lea-rig,
My ain kind dearie O.

Andantino   Tune: The Lea Rig

My Ain Kind Dearie
The Lea Rig

The Lea Rig
was one of eleven songs
which Thomson sent to Burns
remarking on the "coarseness and
vulgarity which the writers of those songs
had confounded with simplicity."
Burns replied, "Let me tell you that you
are too fastidious in your ideas of songs
and ballads. I own that your criticisms
are just~~ but who shall mend the matter?
Who shall rise up and say "Go to! I will
make a better?" For instance on reading over
the Lea Rig, I immediately set about
trying my hand on it, and, after all, I
could make nothing more of it than
the following, which, Heaven
knows, is poor enough."

But pleasures are like poppies spread,
You seize the flow'r, its bloom is shed;
Or like the snow falls in the river
A moment white ~ then melts forever.

All in its rude and prickly bower,
That crimson rose, how sweet and fair;
But love is far a sweeter flower
Amid life's thorny path o' care.

The Red Red Rose

To Edinburgh, in 1784, there came a young Italian music teacher and singer named Pietro Urbani. He had a love for Scottish airs and according to Burns in a letter to Thomson~~~"he sings so delightfully, that whatever he introduces at your concert must have immediate celebrity." He edited a collection of the Song Music of Scotland and in 1793 he published his Selection of Scots Songs.

Burns met him about this time and promised to send him words for airs so long as Johnson and Thomson had first choice. It appears that Urbani was 'borrowing' songs from the Museum, and told Cunningham that he had the full collab-eration of the Bard. Burns denied this in a letter to Cunningham, stating, "Urbani has told a damned falsehood." He did, however, send him the words for a song, and in 1794 "The Red Red Rose" first appeared in Urbani's Scots Songs to an original tune.

It then appeared in Volume 5 of the Museum in 1797 to the tune 'Major Graham's Strath-~spey'~~~~ eighteen months after the death of Burns.

The Red Red Rose

In 1797, the Red Red Rose appeared in Johnson's Musical Museum to the tune of 'Major Graham', the air that Burns had specified. It was not too popular at first.

Air: Low down in the Broom.

Some twenty-five years later it appeared, set to the tune "Low down in the Broom" in the Scottish Minstrel. It has been a favourite ever since.

The Red Red Rose

O my luv's like   a red-red rose,
That's newly   sprung in June;
O my luv's like   the melodie
     That's sweetly play'd in tune.
As fair art thou my bonnie lass,
     Sae deep in love am I;
And I will love thee still my dear,
     Till a' the seas gang dry.

Till a' the seas
     gang dry my dear,
and the rocks melt wi' the sun;
     And I will love thee still my dear,
while the sands   o' life shall run.
And fare thee weel   my only love,
And fare thee weel   a while,
And I will come again   my love
Tho' it were ten thousand mile.

The Red Red Rose

There are several versions of this song ~ a red rose being ever popular with lovers. One of the earliest was composed by a Lieutenant Hinches as a farewell to his sweetheart on the eve of his departure to foreign fields. The Burns improvement is the version that is sung to-day.

Two verses from other poets show why this is so ~~~

"Ten thousand mile is a long, long way,
When from me you are gone;
You leave me here to lament and sigh,
But you never can hear my moan."
"Now fare-thee-well, my dearest love
Till I return on shore;
And thou shalt be my only love
Tho' it were for evermore."

My love for the song began in 1936; a question in my Higher English paper was: Define Hyperbole ~ give an example. My answer was "My love is like a red red rose," and quoted the last verse as an example. The inspector ~ a lady ~ commented, "A good example of 'hyperbole,' Andrew" and then with a smile, "maybe when the time comes you'll change your mind."

Only she and I knew what was written.

Content and love bring peace and joy,
What mair ha'e queens upon a throne?

How slow ye move, ye heavy hours,
The joyless day how dreary!
It wisna sae ye glinted by~
When I was wi' my dearie.

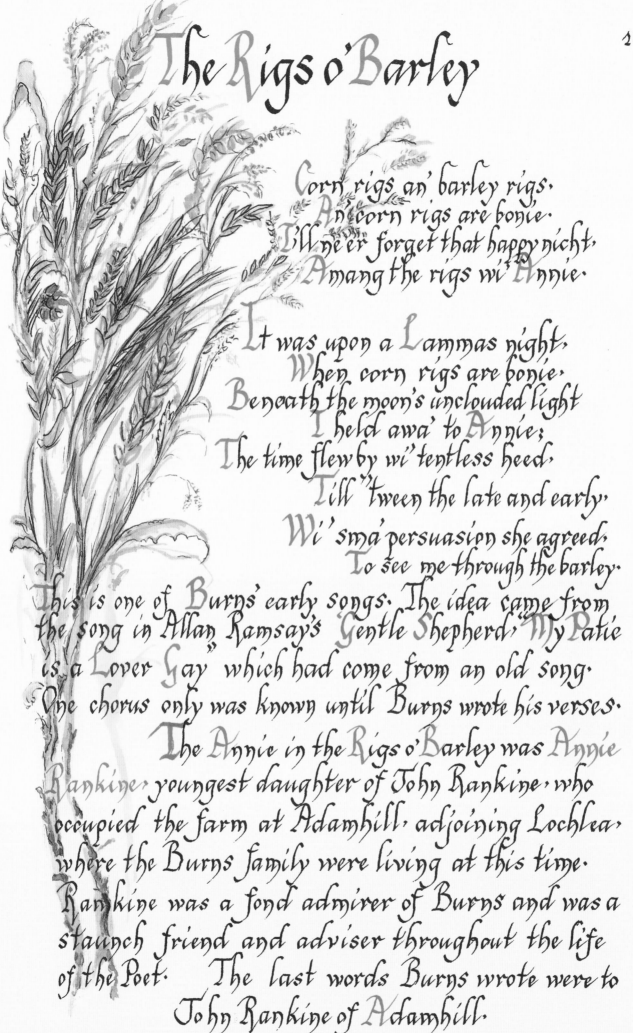

The Rigs o' Barley

Corn rigs an' barley rigs,
An' corn rigs are bonie,
I'll ne'er forget that happy nicht,
Amang the rigs wi' Annie.

It was upon a Lammas night,
When corn rigs are bonie,
Beneath the moon's unclouded light
I held awa' to Annie;
The time flew by wi' tentless heed,
Till 'tween the late and early,
Wi' sma' persuasion she agreed,
To see me through the barley.

This is one of Burns' early songs. The idea came from
the song in Allan Ramsay's "Gentle Shepherd, My Patie
is a Lover Gay" which had come from an old song.
One chorus only was known until Burns wrote his verses.
The Annie in the Rigs o' Barley was Annie
Rankine, youngest daughter of John Rankine, who
occupied the farm at Adamhill, adjoining Lochlea,
where the Burns family were living at this time.
Rankine was a fond admirer of Burns and was a
staunch friend and adviser throughout the life
of the Poet. The last words Burns wrote were to
John Rankine of Adamhill.

The Rigs o' Barley

The sky was blue, the wind was still,
The moon was shining clearly;
I set her down, wi' right good will
Amang the rigs o' barley.
I kent her heart was a' my ain;
I lov'd her most sincerely,
I kissed her ower and ower again,
Amang the rigs o' barley.

I locked her in my fond embrace;
Her heart was beating rarely;
My blessings on that happy place,
Amang the rigs o' barley;
But by the moon and stars so bright
That shone that hour so clearly,
She ay shall bless that happy night
Amang the rigs o' barley.

I hae been blythe wi' comrades dear;
I hae been merry drinking;
I hae been joyfu' gath'rin gear;
I hae been happy thinking:
But a' the pleasures e'er I saw,
Tho' three times doubled fairly
That happy night was worth them a'
Amang the rigs o' barley.

The Rigs o' Barley

Air: Corn Rigs.

Moderato

The Rigs o' Barley

John Rankine always asserted that the Annie in the
Rigs o' Barley was his youngest daughter; he would
add that on meeting Rab after the publication of the song,
Annie had said that she had little expected to be
celebrated by him in print, whereupon he had replied,
"O ay, I was just wanting to give you a cast amang the lave"

Annie married John Merry, an innkeeper in Cumnock.
She died there in 1843. To the end she often sang
her very own song --the Rigs o' Barley -- and always
spoke with affection of memories of the Poet, fifty
years after she first met him at Adamhill.

O wad some Power the giftie gi'e us,
To see oorsels as ithers see us,
It wad frae mony a blunder free us
    An' foolish notion.

Then gently scan your brither man,
Still gentler sister woman;
Tho' they may gang a kennin' wrang
To step aside is human.

To Mary in Heaven

There is no doubt that this song was written for Mary Campbell, when the Bard was in Ellisland. Three years after the death of Mary, Mrs Burns noticed the Bard grow sad about something one September evening; he wandered along the bank of the Nith river and around the stackyard, where he had been working all afternoon. He seemed to be very agitated and, although repeatedly asked to come in out of the cold, he refused to do so and finally settled in the lee of a cornstack.

There he lingered until the cold light of morning, and the stars began to disappear one by one. At this point, Jean prevailed upon him to come to the fireside; almost immediately he entered, went to his desk and wrote, exactly as they are now, with all the ease of one copying from memory, the sublime, imperishable verses of "To Mary in Heaven":

"Still o'er these scenes my mem'ry wakes,
And fondly broods with miser-care;
Time but the impression stronger makes,
As streams their channels deeper wear."

To Mary in Heaven

Air: Mary's Dream (old set)

Thou ling'ring star with less'ning ray
That lov'st to greet the early morn,
Again thou usher'st in the day
My Mary from my soul was torn.
O Mary! dear departed shade,
Where is thy place of blissful rest?
See'st thou thy lover lowly laid?
Hear'st thou the groans that rend his breast?

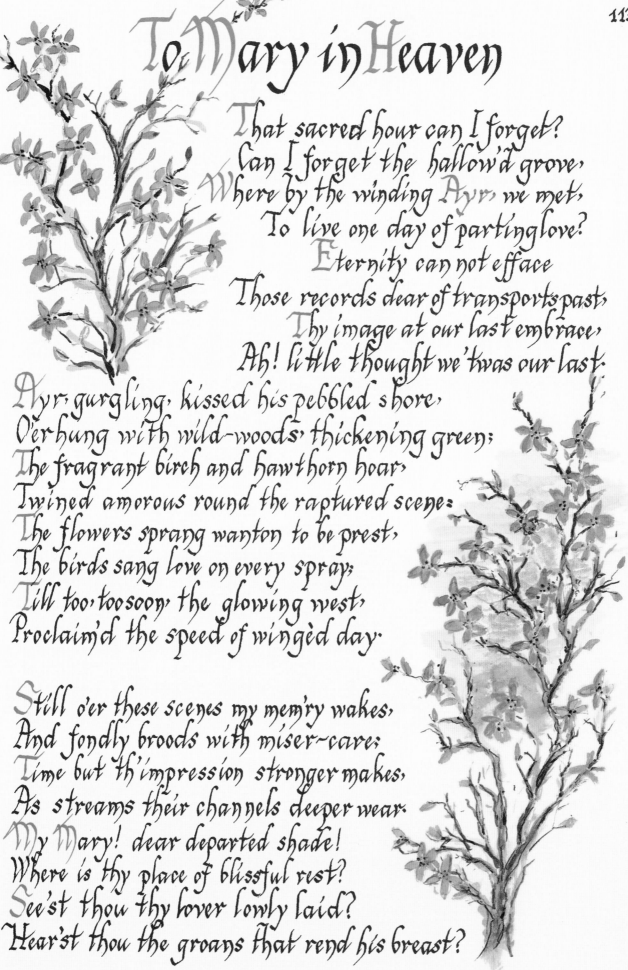

To Mary in Heaven

That sacred hour can I forget?
Can I forget the hallow'd grove,
Where by the winding Ayr we met,
To live one day of parting love?
Eternity can not efface
Those records dear of transports past,
Thy image at our last embrace,
Ah! little thought we 'twas our last.

Ayr, gurgling, kissed his pebbled shore,
O'erhung with wild-woods' thickening green;
The fragrant birch and hawthorn hoar,
Twined amorous round the raptured scene:
The flowers sprang wanton to be prest,
The birds sang love on every spray,
Till too, too soon, the glowing west,
Proclaim'd the speed of wingèd day.

Still o'er these scenes my mem'ry wakes,
And fondly broods with miser-care;
Time but th'impression stronger makes,
As streams their channels deeper wear.
My Mary! dear departed shade!
Where is thy place of blissful rest?
See'st thou thy lover lowly laid?
Hear'st thou the groans that rend his breast?

To Mary in Heaven

"Mary in Heaven" is not sung as often as "Afton Water" but is, however, a great favourite played as a solo on the violin. I remember as a boy, after a week of continual practice, that my teacher shook his head sadly, took my violin and began to play. Quietly, numbly, I sat and listened until two tears ran down my cheeks. When he finished he handed back my fiddle saying ~~ not unkindly ~~ "Just keep playing laddie, and when you're playing "Mary's Dream" just let your fiddle greet."

Will the full story of Mary ever be known? It was an age of badly kept records. There are tales of badly burned or destroyed books and records. The Bibles which the lovers exchanged 'over running water' are now in Alloway — with names smudged and barely recognisable. One has a lock of hair of the 'tall girl with fair hair and blue eyes'.

Of one thing we can be certain ~ this 'pleasant girl with winning ways' was not to know that she would be known to future generations as the Highland Mary who fell in love with Robert Burns.

Then let us pray that come it may,
As come it will, for a'that,
That sense and worth, o'er a' the earth,
May bear the gree and a'that.

For a' that, and a' that,
It's coming yet, for a' that,
That man to man the warld o'er,
Shall brithers be, for a' that.

The Banks o' Doon

This song was sent to Johnson for his *Musical Museum* in 1792. The air was composed by James Miller——a lawyer in Edinburgh. A copy of the song, with a few corrections and harmonizations by Stephen Clarke, was given to Neil Gow, who printed it in his 1788 collection of Strathspey Reels under the name of the "Caledonian Hunt's Delight." It is interesting to note that this title is scored out in the manuscript in the British Museum.

Burns wanted this song to appear in the First Edinburgh Edition of his poems, but a note explains why this was not to be —— "My two songs on —— —— were tried yesterday by a jury of literati and found defamatory libels against the fastidious powers of Poesy and Taste, and the author forbidden to print them under pain of forfeiture of character. I cannot help shedding a tear to the memory of two songs that had cost me some pains, and that I valued a good deal; but I must submit."

The song was accepted later and is now one of the best known of all the songs of Burns.

The Banks o' Doon

Ye banks and braes o' bonie Doon,
how can ye bloom sae fresh and fair?
How can ye chant, ye little birds,
and I sae weary, fu' o' care?

Thou'll break my heart, thou warbling bird
that wantons thro' the flow'ring thorn,
Thou minds me o' departed joys ~~~
departed, never to return.

Aft hae I roved by bonie Doon
to see the rose and woodbine twine;
And ilka bird sang o' its Love,
and fondly sae did I o' mine;

Wi' lichtsome heart I pu'ed a rose,
fu' sweet upon its thorny tree,
But my fause Luver staw my rose
and ah, he left the thorn wi' me.

The Banks o' Doon

Air   *The Caledonian Hunt's Delight.*

The Banks o' Doon

The Banks o' Doon was written by Burns for Peggy Kennedy, the sister of Gavin Hamilton's wife. The poet first met her at Gavin's house when she was a lass of eighteen. At that time she was being courted by Captain Andrew M'Doual, and some nine years later, in 1794, she bore him a daughter. Despite pleadings from Peggy that a form of private marriage had taken place, the Captain denied both paternity and marriage.

An action was raised, but Peggy died of a broken heart before it was concluded. Three years later the Consistorial Court declared in favour of the marriage and the legitimacy of the child. This decision, however, was reversed by the Court of Session, who none-the-less awarded damages of £3000 to the dead woman and alimentary provision for the child.

The music, words and story combine to make this one of the favourite songs sung by Scots throughout the world.

Is there beneath loves noble name
can harbour dark the selfish aim
to bless himself alone?

We'll sing auld Coila's plains an' fells,
Her moors red brown wi' heather bells,
Her banks and braes, her dens and dells.

Auld Lang Syne

For auld lang syne, my dear,
For auld lang syne;
We'll tak a cup o' kindness yet
For auld lang syne. *Chorus*

In a list of notes on songs to Thomson, Burns states "One more song and I have done ~ Auld lang syne ~ the old song of the olden times — I took it down from an old man's singing;" and again to Mrs Dunlop, he writes ~~ "Is not the Scotch phrase Auld lang syne exceedingly expressive?" There is an old song and tune which has often thrilled through my soul."

Should auld acquaintance be forgot,
and never brought to mind?
Should auld acquaintance be forgot,
and auld lang syne?

And surely ye'll be your pint stowp
and surely I'll be mine!
And we'll tak a cup o' kindness yet
for auld lang syne.

Auld Lang Syne

We twa ha'e run aboot the braes
and pou'd the gowans fine:
But we've wandered mony a weary fitt,
sin' auld lang syne.

We twa ha'e paidl'd in the burn
frae morning sun till dine;
But seas between us braid ha'e roar'd
sin auld lang syne.

And there's a hand, my trusty fiere!
and gie's a hand o' thine!
And we'll tak a right gude-willie waught,
for auld lang syne.

I have a fond hope that one day the chorus of this song
will be sung correctly throughout the world. There
is no "we'll meet again some ither nicht."   There
is no "for the sake of" or "for the days of", but quite simply
"We'll tak a cup o' kindness yet
For auld lang syne."

Auld Lang Syne

"Auld Lang Syne" has taken the place of another old song ~~~
"Good night, and joy be wi' you a'."

Not too slow   Tune: I fee'd a lad at Michaelmas

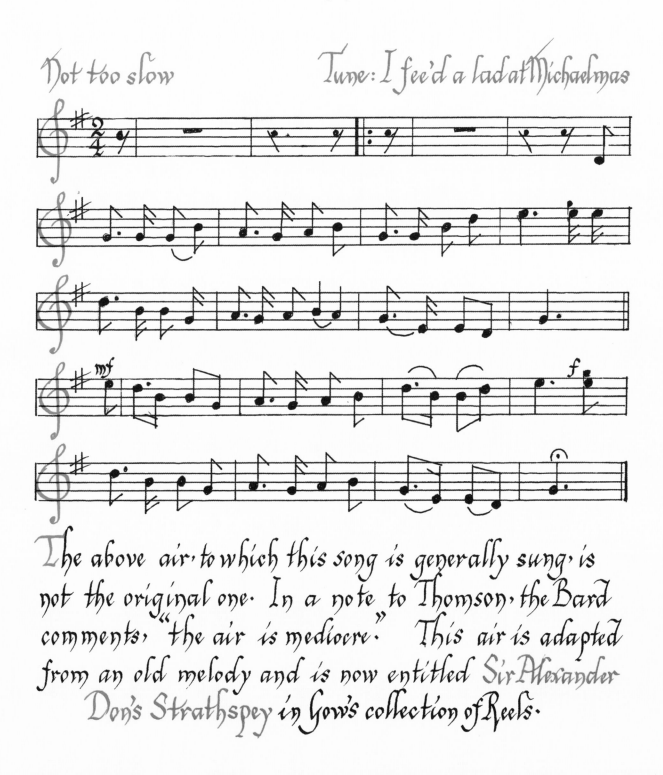

The above air to which this song is generally sung, is not the original one. In a note to Thomson, the Bard comments, "the air is mediocre." This air is adapted from an old melody and is now entitled Sir Alexander Don's Strathspey in Gow's collection of Reels.

Auld Lang Syne

For many years, Burns was intrigued with the theme of auld lang syne. From late fifteenth century our poets had voiced this typically "guid nicht" parting song. A recent version by Allan Ramsay
~~~~ Should auld acquaintance be forgot,
Though they return with scars,
These are the noble hero's lot,
Obtained in glorious wars. ~~~~ bears
no resemblance to the refined song which Burns sent to Johnson and Thomson.

Before we part, let us stand, form a circle ~~~ and sing ~~~ hand to hand ~~~ "We'll tak' a cup o' kindness yet,
For auld lang syne."

From scenes like these, old Scotia's grandeur springs,
That makes her loved at home, revered abroad;
Princes and lords are but the breath of kings,
An honest man's the noblest work of God.